The Night Before Christmas

ILLUSTRATED BY JANE CHAMBLESS

Distributed by Funk & Wagnalls

'Twas the night before Christmas,
when all through the house
Not a creature was stirring,
not even a mouse;
The stockings were hung
by the chimney with care,
In hopes that St. Nicholas
soon would be there.

The children were nestled
all snug in their beds,

While visions of sugar-plums
danced in their heads;

When out on the lawn
there arose such a clatter,
I sprang from my bed to see
what was the matter.
When, what to my wondering
eyes should appear,
But a miniature sleigh,
and eight tiny reindeer,

With a little old driver, so lively and quick,
I knew in a moment it must be St. Nick.
"Now, Dasher! Now, Dancer!
Now, Prancer and Vixen!
On, Comet! On, Cupid!
On, Donder and Blitzen!
To the top of the porch!
To the top of the wall!
Now dash away! Dash away!
Dash away all!"

And then in a twinkling, I heard on the roof,
The prancing and pawing of each little hoof.
As I drew in my head,
and was turning around,
Down the chimney St. Nicholas
came with a bound.

He had a broad face and a round little belly,
That shook when he laughed,
like a bowl full of jelly.
He was chubby and plump,
a right jolly old elf,
And I laughed when I saw him,
in spite of myself.

He spoke not a word,
but went straight to his work,
And filled all the stockings;
then turned with a jerk,
And laying his finger aside of his nose,
And giving a nod, up the chimney he rose;
He sprang to his sleigh,
to his team gave a whistle,
And away they all flew like the down
of a thistle,

But I heard him exclaim
as he drove out of sight,
"HAPPY CHRISTMAS TO ALL,
AND TO ALL A GOOD NIGHT!"